Who can I play with?

Adapted by: Pamela Egan
Pictures: Dea de Vries

Ben is bored.
He is bored with his train.
He is bored with his ball.
His painting book is full.
He has nobody to play with.
'I'm bored!' says Ben.

'Never mind,' says Dad.
'You start school tomorrow.'
'What will school be like?'
   asks Ben.
'Not boring,' says Dad.
'There will be children
   to play with.'

Today is Ben's big day.
He is off to school.
'Mum, will there be toys
   at school?' asks Ben.
'Yes, lots of toys,' says Mum.
'Let's go and see.'

Here is Ben's school.
'Hello, Ben! How nice
   to see you!'
Who's that?
Miss Jones, the teacher.
Ben thinks she looks nice.
But he feels a bit shy.
What happens now?

'This is Peter,' says Miss Jones.
'Peter, this is Ben.
'Peter will look after you.'
'Hello, Ben,' says Peter.
'Come and see our big crane.'

The crane is very big indeed.
It is enormous!
Ben wants to play with it.
There is a toy garage
   full of cars.
Ben wants that too.
He grabs the crane.
He sits on the garage.
Nobody else can have them!

All the children are playing.
They are playing together.
Some are playing house.
Some are making models.
Some are making pastry.
They are all happy.
They like doing things together.

Ben watches a boy and a girl.
They are making a tall tower.
They are making it together.
The tower is wobbling.
Will it fall?
Not yet . . .
Yes.
CRASH!
What do they say?
'Let's do it again!'

A boy comes up to Ben.
He says, 'Can I put
    my car in the garage?'
'No,' says Ben.
'I'm playing with
    the garage.'
Another boy says,
'Can we have the crane?'
'No,' says Ben.
He hugs the crane hard.
He sits on the garage —
    bump!
Now nobody can play
    with the toys.
Not even Ben!

'Make a circle and we'll sing,'
    says Miss Jones.
Ben sits still.
The children hold out their hands to him.
'Come and sing with us, Ben!' they say.
Ben gets up slowly.
He holds hands with the children.

They sing, 'This is the way we dance along,
Dance along, dance along,
This is the way we dance along,
As we sing together.'

'Let's clap!' says Peter.
So they sing, 'This is the way we clap our
    hands . . .'
Then the teacher says,
'Ben, what shall we do now? You say!'

'Let's play a game,' says Ben.
'Good idea,' says Miss Jones.
'What shall we play?'
'Tig,' says somebody.
'Hide and seek,' says somebody else.
Playing games is fun.
Ben loves it.

Ben is back at the garage.
But he isn't sitting on it.
He is playing with two other boys.
They are loading the lorries together.
'Come home with me after school,'
  says Ben.
'We can play with my train.'
Playing together is fun.
Ben loves it.

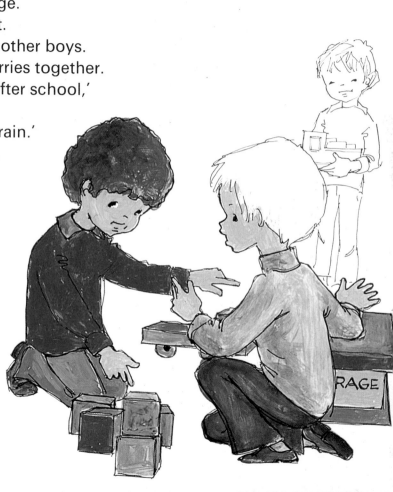

Notes for parents and teachers:

We are born into a world which Christians
believe was created for all men to share. The
idea of 'sharing', however, does not come
naturally to the under-seven, whose world
centres on himself, and if he has not been
accustomed to a large family or to life in a
playgroup, the give-and-take required at school
can come as a real shock. He needs to be helped
to share not because he 'ought to', but because
there is a real joy to be found in giving pleasure
and help to others. The child who understands
what it is to give and to share with love will
come in later years to understand better the total
self-giving of Jesus for the world he loves.